General Certificate of Secondary Education

GCSE
Science: Double Award
(Coordinated)
Paper 1 – *Higher Tier*

Centre name					
Centre number					
Candidate number					

Chemistry

Surname
Other names
Candidate signature

Time allowed: 1 hour 30 minutes.

CW00556791

Instructions to candidates
- Write your name and other details in the spaces provided above.
- Answer **all** questions in the spaces provided.
- Do all rough work on the paper.
- Write your answers in black or blue ink or ball-point pen.

Information for candidates
- The marks available are given in brackets at the end of each question or part-question.
- Marks will not be deducted for incorrect answers.
- In calculations show clearly how you work out your answers.
- State the units in all your answers.
- There are 11 questions in this paper. There are two blank pages.

Advice to candidates
- Work steadily through the paper.
- Don't spend too long on one question.
- If you have time at the end, go back and check your answers.

For examiner's use

Q	Attempt Nº 1	2	3	Q	Attempt Nº 1	2	3
1				8			
2				9			
3				10			
4				11			
5							
6							
7							
				Total 100			

Periodic Table of the Elements

The volume of one mole of any gas at room temperature and pressure (r.t.p.) is 24 dm^3.

Key:

Relative atomic mass A	1
Atomic symbol	**H**
Name	Hydrogen
Atomic number (proton number) Z	1

Period	Group I	Group II											Group III	Group IV	Group V	Group VI	Group VII	Group 0
1																		4 **He** Helium 2
2	7 **Li** Lithium 3	9 **Be** Beryllium 4											11 **B** Boron 5	12 **C** Carbon 6	14 **N** Nitrogen 7	16 **O** Oxygen 8	19 **F** Fluorine 9	20 **Ne** Neon 10
3	23 **Na** Sodium 11	24 **Mg** Magnesium 12											27 **Al** Aluminium 13	28 **Si** Silicon 14	31 **P** Phosphorus 15	32 **S** Sulphur 16	35.5 **Cl** Chlorine 17	40 **Ar** Argon 18
4	39 **K** Potassium 19	40 **Ca** Calcium 20	45 **Sc** Scandium 21	48 **Ti** Titanium 22	51 **V** Vanadium 23	52 **Cr** Chromium 24	55 **Mn** Manganese 25	56 **Fe** Iron 26	59 **Co** Cobalt 27	59 **Ni** Nickel 28	64 **Cu** Copper 29	65 **Zn** Zinc 30	70 **Ga** Gallium 31	73 **Ge** Germanium 32	75 **As** Arsenic 33	79 **Se** Selenium 34	80 **Br** Bromine 35	84 **Kr** Krypton 36
5	85 **Rb** Rubidium 37	88 **Sr** Strontium 38	89 **Y** Yttrium 39	91 **Zr** Zirconium 40	93 **Nb** Niobium 41	96 **Mo** Molybdenum 42	98 **Tc** Technetium 43	101 **Ru** Ruthenium 44	103 **Rh** Rhodium 45	106 **Pd** Palladium 46	108 **Ag** Silver 47	112 **Cd** Cadmium 48	115 **In** Indium 49	119 **Sn** Tin 50	122 **Sb** Antimony 51	128 **Te** Tellurium 52	127 **I** Iodine 53	131 **Xe** Xenon 54
6	133 **Cs** Caesium 55	137 **Ba** Barium 56	139 **La** Lanthanum 57	178.5 **Hf** Hafnium 72	181 **Ta** Tantalum 73	184 **W** Tungsten 74	186 **Re** Rhenium 75	190 **Os** Osmium 76	192 **Ir** Iridium 77	195 **Pt** Platinum 78	197 **Au** Gold 79	201 **Hg** Mercury 80	204 **Tl** Thallium 81	207 **Pb** Lead 82	209 **Bi** Bismuth 83	210 **Po** Polonium 84	210 **At** Astatine 85	222 **Rn** Radon 86
7	223 **Fr** Francium 87	226 **Ra** Radium 88	227 **Ac** Actinium 89															

The Lanthanides	140 **Ce** Cerium 58	141 **Pr** Praseodymium 59	144 **Nd** Neodymium 60	147 **Pm** Promethium 61	150 **Sm** Samarium 62	152 **Eu** Europium 63	157 **Gd** Gadolinium 64	159 **Tb** Terbium 65	162 **Dy** Dysprosium 66	165 **Ho** Holmium 67	167 **Er** Erbium 68	169 **Tm** Thulium 69	173 **Yb** Ytterbium 70	175 **Lu** Lutetium 71
The Actinides	232 **Th** Thorium 90	231 **Pa** Protactinium 91	238 **U** Uranium 92	237 **Np** Neptunium 93	242 **Pu** Plutonium 94	243 **Am** Americium 95	247 **Cm** Curium 96	247 **Bk** Berkelium 97	251 **Cf** Californium 98	254 **Es** Einsteinium 99	253 **Fm** Fermium 100	256 **Md** Mendelevium 101	254 **No** Nobelium 102	257 **Lr** Lawrencium 103

1 The diagram below shows the arrangement of electrons in an atom of potassium.

Leave blank

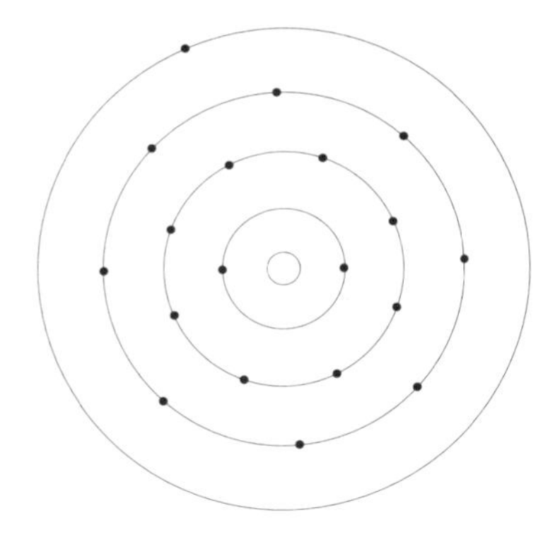

(a) Complete the table below.

	number of protons	number of neutrons	number of electrons	electron arrangement
Potassium-39	19	20	19	2, 8, 8, 1
Chlorine-35	~~16~~ 17	18	16	2, 8, 6

(3 marks)

(b) Potassium chloride has ionic bonding.
Explain exactly what happens when potassium chloride is formed, in terms of the transfer of electrons.

2,8,8 Potassium loses 1 electron from its outer shell, and it is gained by Chlorine. Potassium becomes
2,8,8 positively charged. Chlorine becomes negatively charged Attracted to each other to form potassium chloride.

(4 marks)

(c) Calcium oxide also has ionic bonding (it contains Ca^{2+} and O^{2-} ions), and it has a similar structure to potassium chloride. Its melting point is 2614 °C, compared to 870 °C for potassium chloride.
Suggest why the melting points of these two similar compounds are so different.

Bond in $Ca^{2+}O^{2-}$ is stronger than K^+Cl^- because both the ions have twice the charge. So needs more energy hence higher C° to break bonds.

(2 marks)

Leave blank

(ii) Write down a common use for each of these two elements.

Iron: steel production, cars.

Copper: alloys, saucepans wires

(2 marks)

(iii) Give one other property commonly shared by transition elements.

High MP + BP.

(1 mark)

10 Acid rain is a major cause of damage to limestone and marble buildings in some cities.

(a) (i) Name a gas that causes acid rain.

....

(1 mark)

(ii) Write down a balanced equation for the reaction in which the acid is formed.

....

(2 marks)

(iii) Explain how acid rain might affect a limestone building.

....

....

(2 marks)

(b) Give one way in which the formation of acid rain can be reduced.

....

(1 mark)

Another environmental problem caused by acid rain is the acidification of lakes and soils, which can kill fish and plants. One way to limit the damage is to add slaked lime (calcium hydroxide) to the lake or soil, to neutralise the acid.

(c) Write down a balanced equation for the reaction that takes place when an acidic lake is neutralised by adding slaked lime.

....

(2 marks)

Leave blank

11 The diagram below shows sodium chloride solution being electrolysed.

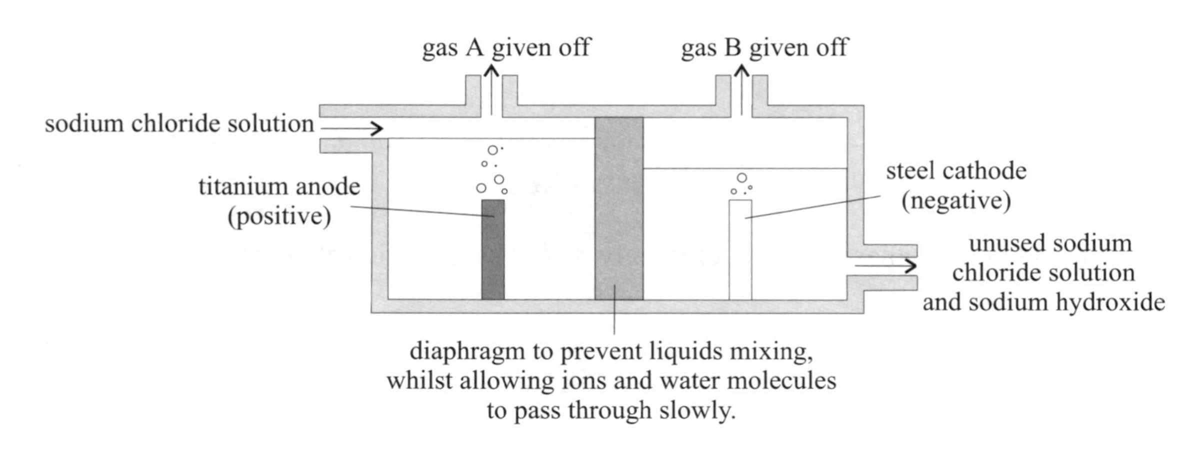

(a) (i) What is the common name for sodium chloride?

....

(1 mark)

(ii) Write down the chemical formula for sodium chloride.

....

(1 mark)

(b) In this experiment, the sodium chloride is dissolved in water.
What does that tell you about the structure of sodium chloride?

....

(1 mark)

(c) (i) Name the gases A and B which are given off during this experiment.

A: .... B: ....

(2 marks)

(ii) Give one use for each of these gases.

A: ....

B: ....

(2 marks)

(d) Write down the balanced ionic equations at the anode and cathode.

Anode: ....

Cathode: ....

(4 marks)

Leave blank

BLANK PAGE

Leave blank

(iii) Explain why ethanol can be used as a fuel. Use ideas about the energy changes that occur when bonds are made and broken in your answer.

....

....

....

....

(4 marks)

5 Cracking is a very important process in industry. An example of a cracking reaction is shown below.

$$C_8H_{18} \longrightarrow C_5H_{12} + C_3H_6$$

(a) Explain what is meant by **cracking**.

....

....

....

(2 marks)

(b) Many unsaturated hydrocarbons can be used to manufacture plastics.

(i) Give an example of an **unsaturated** hydrocarbon.

....

(1 mark)

(ii) Explain what is meant by the term **unsaturated**.

....

....

(1 mark)

(c) Explain why plastics can be manufactured from unsaturated hydrocarbons, but not from saturated hydrocarbons.

....

....

(1 mark)

Leave blank

6 Iron and tin are both used to make a variety of everyday items.

(a) The table below gives some information about iron and tin.

Metal	Cost per 10 kg (£)	Amount in Earth's crust (%)
Tin	95	0.0002
Iron	1.70	5

(i) Look at the above table and give two reasons why it is important to recycle tin.

1. ....

2. ....

(2 marks)

Steel is made by combining iron with small amounts of other elements.
A very large proportion of steel used is recycled.

(ii) Which property of iron (and steel) makes it particularly easy to separate steel from other types of waste products?

....

(1 mark)

(b) Galvanising is the process of adding a protective layer of zinc onto the surface of steel. This protects the steel underneath even if the zinc coating is scratched or damaged.

(i) Explain why even a scratched coating of zinc can help protect the steel underneath. You should refer to the reactivity series of metals in your answer.

....

....

....

....

(3 marks)

A similar kind of protection is used on underwater pipelines.
Blocks of metal are attached in order to protect the steel pipe.

(ii) Which of these metals could be used for the protective blocks?

magnesium or **copper**

....

(1 mark)

Leave blank

7 Hydrogen reacts with chlorine to form hydrogen chloride.
This reaction is exothermic.

(a) What is meant by the term **exothermic**?

....

....

(1 mark)

(b) Look at the equation below, and the structures of the molecules involved in the reaction.

hydrogen + chlorine ⟶ hydrogen chloride

H—H + Cl/Cl ⟶ H—Cl H—Cl

The bond energies for the bonds in the above molecules are:

H—H: 436 kJ/mole Cl—Cl: 242 kJ/mole H—Cl: 431 kJ/mole

Calculate the energy released if 1 mole of hydrogen and 1 mole of chlorine react to form 2 moles of hydrogen chloride.

....

....

....

....

(2 marks)

Turn over for next question.

8 When iron corrodes, it turns into iron oxide. This iron oxide can be turned back into iron again by heating it in a furnace with hydrogen. A simplified equation for the reaction is shown below.

$$Fe_2O_3 + 3H_2 \longrightarrow 2Fe + 3H_2O$$

(a) If a corroded iron sword is heated with hydrogen in this way, what will happen to the mass of the sword? Explain your answer.

....

....

....

(2 marks)

(b) (i) What mass of iron will combine with 48 g of oxygen to make Fe_2O_3?
(O = 16, Fe = 56)

....

....

Mass: .... *g*

(1 mark)

(ii) What mass of hydrogen is needed in order to produce 112 g of iron? Show your working. (H = 1, Fe = 56)

....

....

Mass: .... *g*

(3 marks)

(c) This reaction goes faster at higher temperatures. Explain why this is the case.

....

....

(2 marks)

(d) There are different kinds of iron oxide, but they all react with hydrogen in a similar way. If you start with Fe_3O_4, write a balanced equation for the reaction between this oxide of iron and hydrogen.

....

(3 marks)

Leave blank

Leave blank

(e) Iron(III) oxide (Fe_2O_3) is an ionic compound. Ionic compounds generally have high melting points.

(i) Explain why this is.

....

....
(1 mark)

(ii) Sodium chloride (NaCl) and magnesium oxide (MgO) are also ionic compounds, but the melting point of magnesium oxide is higher than that of sodium chloride.

Explain why.

....

....
(2 marks)

9 A chemical compound contains only carbon and hydrogen. It was found that 100 g of this compound contained 85.7 g of carbon.

(a) (i) Calculate the mass of hydrogen contained in 100 g of the compound.

....
(1 mark)

(ii) Use this information to calculate the number of moles of carbon atoms and hydrogen atoms in 100 g of the compound.

....

Carbon: .... *moles*

Hydrogen: .... *moles*
(1 mark)

(iii) Use this information to find the simplest formula possible for the compound.

....
(2 marks)

(b) The mass of 1 mole of the compound is 84 g. What is the molecular formula of the compound?

....

Formula: ....
(2 marks)

10 The following equations describe some reactions of acids.

A $6HCl + 2Al \longrightarrow 2AlCl_3 + 3H_2$

B $H_2SO_4 + Na_2CO_3 \longrightarrow Na_2SO_4 + H_2O + CO_2$

C $H_2SO_4 + 2KOH \longrightarrow K_2SO_4 + 2H_2O$

D $2HNO_3 + MgO \longrightarrow Mg(NO_3)_2 + H_2O$

(a) Answer the questions below by choosing one of the equations **A**, **B**, **C** or **D**. You can use a letter once, more than once, or not at all.

(i) Which reaction is between a hydroxide and an acid? ☐

(ii) Which reaction produces a nitrate? ☐

(iii) Which reaction produces a gas that turns limewater milky? ☐

(iv) Which reaction produces an explosive colourless gas? ☐

(4 marks)

(b) Equation **C** can be written as an ionic equation.

$$H^+ + OH^- \longrightarrow H_2O$$

Write equation **A** as an ionic equation.

....

(2 marks)

(c) Ammonium nitrate fertiliser can be made by combining ammonia with nitric acid. The word equation below shows how they combine.

ammonia + nitric acid ⟶ ammonium nitrate

Write a balanced chemical equation for this reaction.

....

(2 marks)

Leave blank

Diamond is made of carbon atoms bonded together in a giant covalent structure.

Leave blank

(c) (i) Draw a diagram in the space below, showing the bonds between the carbon atoms in diamond.

Draw the atoms and bonds like the ones shown in the box below.

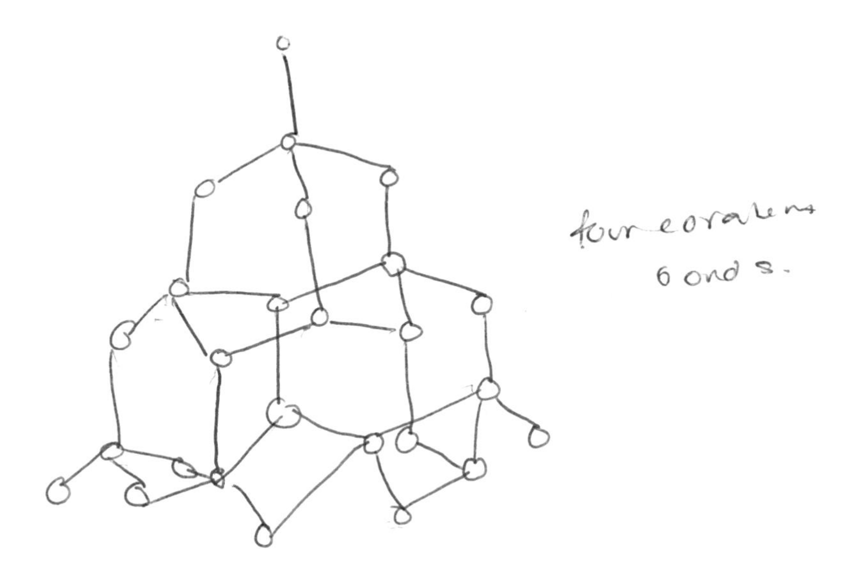

Carbon atom = ●
Covalent bond = —

(2 marks)

(ii) Describe **two** properties of diamond and explain how each property relates to its giant covalent structure.

1. Hig M.P + B.P. as bonds between them are Stronger and takes alot of energy to break them.

2. Does not conduct electricity as there are no free electrons to carry an electric current.

(4 marks)

Leave blank

3 Magnesium metal reacts with dilute hydrochloric acid to make magnesium chloride solution and hydrogen gas.

(a) Balance the equation below for this reaction.

$$Mg(s) + HCl(aq) \rightarrow MgCl_2(aq) + H_2(g)$$

(1 mark)

(b) 0.2 g of magnesium ribbon was added to 100 cm^3 of dilute hydrochloric acid. The amount of hydrogen gas released was measured over time.

(i) At the end of the experiment, all the magnesium had been used up. What does this tell you about the amount of acid used?

....

(1 mark)

The results of the experiment are shown on the graph below.

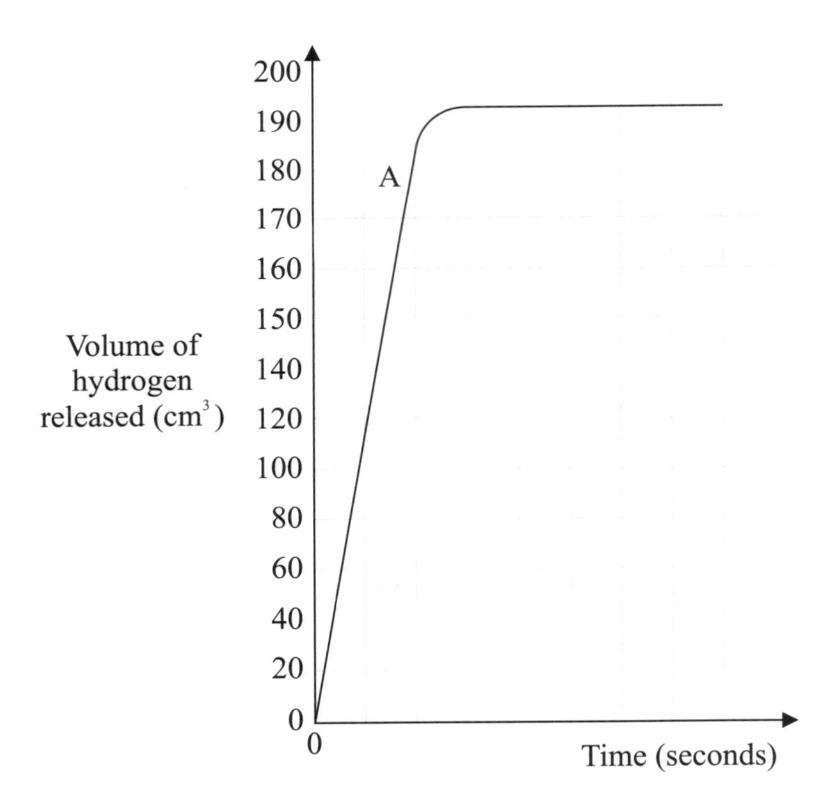

The experiment was repeated twice, first using 70 cm^3 of the same dilute hydrochloric acid and 30 cm^3 of water.
The second time, 40 cm^3 of the acid was used with 60 cm^3 of water.
The amount of magnesium ribbon used remained at 0.2 g for each experiment.
You may assume that the acid remains in excess.

Leave blank

(ii) Repeating the experiment with these changes will allow us to investigate the effect of which factor on the rate of reaction?

....

(1 mark)

(iii) Draw on the graph opposite how you would expect the graph from the two repeats of the experiment to look.
Label the second experiment B and the third experiment C.

(2 marks)

(c) Suggest two other ways that the experiment could be made to go faster.
Explain, in terms of particle collisions, why each of these changes would speed up the reaction.

1. ....

....

....

2. ....

....

....

(4 marks)

4 (a) Look at the diagram below, showing the energy change involved in a chemical reaction. One line shows the reaction taking place without a catalyst, the other line shows the same reaction with a catalyst.

Leave blank

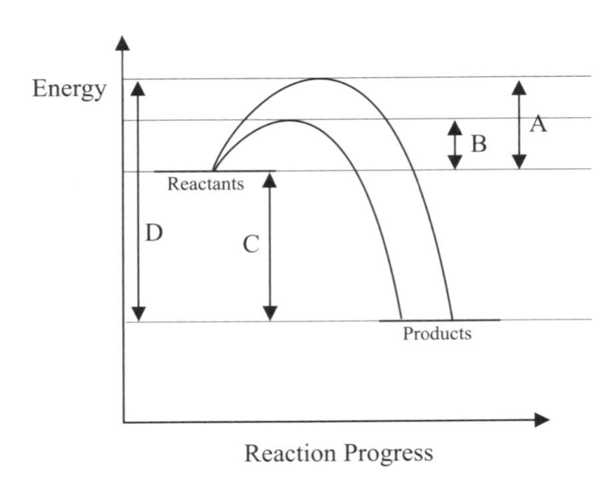

(i) Is this reaction endothermic or exothermic? Explain your answer.

....

....
(2 marks)

Which letter on the diagram represents

(ii) the activation energy of the reaction when a catalyst is used? ....
(1 mark)

(iii) the overall energy change? ....
(1 mark)

(b) Catalytic converters are fitted to new cars to cut down on emissions of pollutant gases.

(i) Name **one** catalyst used in catalytic converters.

Platinum..
(1 mark)

(ii) Write a balanced equation showing how carbon monoxide reacts with oxygen in the air to form a less harmful gas.

$2CO + O_2 \rightarrow 2CO_2$ ....
(2 marks)

Iron is used as a catalyst in the Haber Process.

Leave blank

(c) Give **two** ways in which a catalyst can help to reduce costs in industrial reactions.

1. lowers temp needed – pressure

2. saves time.

(2 marks)

5 There are three types of rock — sedimentary, igneous and metamorphic.

(a) Describe how sedimentary rocks are formed.

....

....

....

(3 marks)

(b) One of the most common sedimentary rocks is often formed from crushed seashells. It is grey/white in colour and composed mainly of calcium carbonate. What is the common name of this rock?

....

(1 mark)

(c) Which of the three types of rock is slate?

....

(1 mark)

Leave blank

6 (a) A chemical compound has the following composition by mass.

Carbon 9.9 % Fluorine 31.4% Chlorine 58.7%

Calculate the empirical formula of this compound.

....

....

....
(2 marks)

(b) The compound from part (a) is a CFC.

(i) Explain how CFCs can cause damage to the Earth's upper atmosphere.

....

....

....
(2 marks)

(ii) How does this damage to the atmosphere increase certain health risks for humans?

....

....
(1 mark)

(c) CFC damage to the Earth's atmosphere is a global environmental problem.
Another global environmental problem is called the Greenhouse Effect.

(i) Which is the main gas responsible for the Greenhouse Effect?

....
(1 mark)

(ii) The Greenhouse Effect is causing the Earth to gradually get warmer.
Describe **two** of the serious global consequences that could result from this gradual change of climate.

1. ....

2. ....
(2 marks)

Leave blank

7 Aluminium is extracted from its ore, bauxite (Al_2O_3), by electrolysis.
The bauxite is dissolved in molten cryolite. The electrodes are made from graphite.

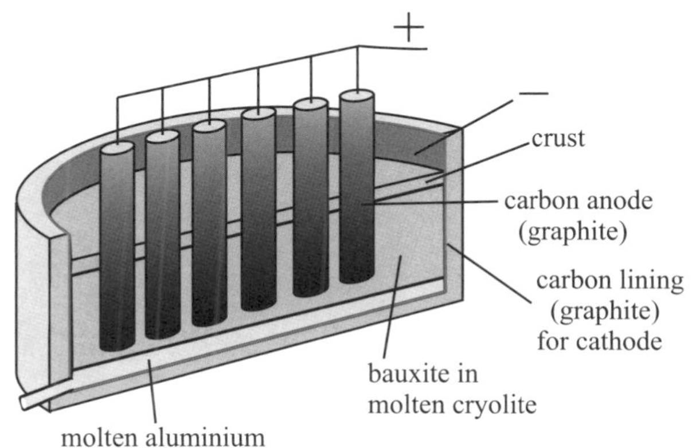

(a) Why is the bauxite dissolved in molten cryolite instead of using pure molten bauxite?

lower temp is required cheaper.

(1 mark)

(b) The graphite anodes gradually get used up and need replacing. How are they used up?

carbon reacts – into carbon dioxide

(1 mark)

(c) Write down "half equations" to show what happens at the anode and the cathode.

At the anode: $2O^{2-} \rightarrow O_2 + 4e^-$

At the cathode: $Al^{3+} + 3e^- \rightarrow Al$.

(3 marks)

(d) Electrolysis of aluminium ore is very expensive. Explain why this is the case.

High temp need – so alot of electricity is needed.

(1 mark)

(e) Aluminium is used in the bodywork of most aeroplanes.
Give **three** properties of aluminium that make it well-suited for this purpose.

1. resistant to corossion

2. strong

3. lightweight.

(3 marks)

8 (a) For each transition metal below, give a **common use** and **one property** that makes it suited for that purpose:

Leave blank

(i) Copper

~~used~~ in Electrical cable - good conductor of electricity.

(2 marks)

(ii) Chromium

stainless steel, strengthens iron.

(2 marks)

(b) Transition metals form very colourful compounds.
Certain precious gemstones get their colour from the presence of transition metals.
Give **two** examples of such gemstones.

Emerald ruby.

(2 marks)

(c) One of the most commonly used metals, iron, will rust in the presence of air and water.
Rust is formed by the iron being oxidised to form iron(III) oxide (Fe_2O_3).

Write a balanced symbol equation to show how rust is formed from iron.
Use this word equation to help.

iron + oxygen ⟶ iron(III) oxide

$2Fe_2 3O_2 \rightarrow 4Fe_2O_3$

(2 marks)

(d) The transition metal nickel is often used to make coins. Suggest why nickel is used for this purpose rather than a Group I metal such as sodium.

Nickel is much less reactive. So coins made from nickel will last longer than coins made from sodium. Group I metals are so

(3 marks)

reactive that, as coins, they'd be dangerous.

Leave blank

9 (a) Draw a diagram to show how the electrons are arranged in a fluorine atom.

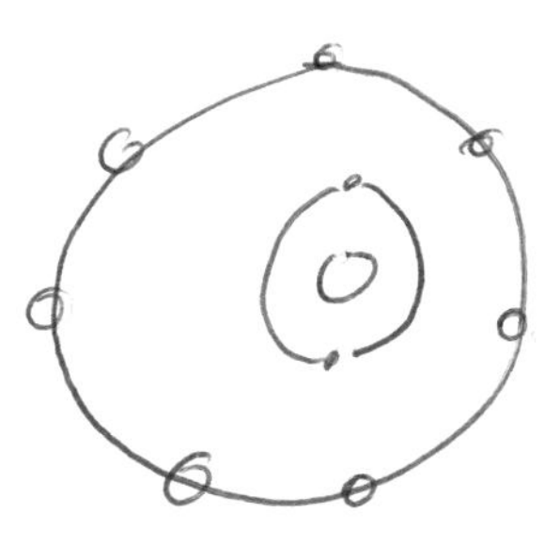

2,7

(1 mark)

(b) Molecules of bromine and molecules of fluorine will react together to form bromine fluoride molecules.

$$Br—Br + F—F \rightarrow Br—F + Br—F$$

1 mole of bromine molecules reacts with 1 mole of fluorine molecules.
During this reaction, 208 kJ of energy are released.
The bond energy for Br — Br is 193 kJ/mol, the bond energy for F — F is 159 kJ/mol.

(i) Calculate the **total** amount of energy required to break the bonds in 1 mole of bromine molecules and 1 mole of fluorine molecules.

....

(1 mark)

(ii) Calculate the bond energy of the Br — F bond.

....

(3 marks)

(c) Fluorine and bromine are halogens (Group VII elements). In their elemental form, the halogens are poisonous. However halogens form compounds which can be very useful to us. Give **one** use of each of these halogens.

(i) Fluorine

....

(1 mark)

(ii) Chlorine

....

(1 mark)

(iii) Iodine

....

(1 mark)

Leave blank

10 (a) The diagram below shows the structure of an atom of a certain element.

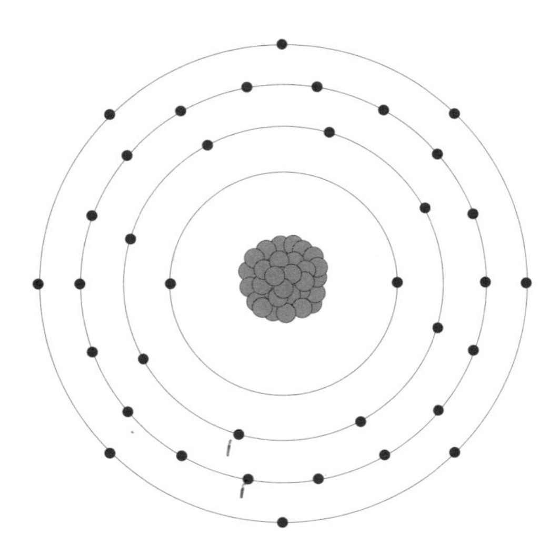

(i) Which group of the Periodic Table is this element in?

noble

(1 mark)

(ii) How many protons are contained in the nucleus of this atom?

36.

(1 mark)

(iii) The nucleus contains 48 neutrons. What is the mass number of this element?

36 + 48 = 84.

(1 mark)

(b) This element is called a noble, or inert gas.

(i) What is meant by the term **inert**?

Unreactive

(1 mark)

(ii) Explain in terms of electron structure why this gas is inert.

has a full outer shell, so doesnt need to lose/gain electrons. therefore dont react.

(2 marks)

(c) Give a **use** of each of these noble gases, and state a **property** of the gas that make it particularly suited for that use.

Leave blank

(i) Argon

fill light bulbs, unreactive gas stops filament from burning away.

(2 marks)

(ii) Helium

Airships, has low density, so it floats.

(2 marks)

Turn over for next question.

11 Ammonia is produced industrially by the Haber Process.
This process uses the reversible reaction shown below.

$$N_2(g) + 3H_2(g) \rightleftharpoons 2NH_3(g)$$

(a) Explain what is meant by the terms **reversible reaction** and **yield**.

Reversible reaction: ....

Yield: ....
(2 marks)

(b) Explain why an operating pressure of 200 atmospheres is used in the Haber Process.

....

....
(2 marks)

(c) In this reaction, lower temperatures favour the forward reaction. Despite this, the temperature used in the industrial manufacture of ammonia is fairly high at 450 °C. Explain why this is the case.

....

....
(2 marks)

(d) Ammonia oxidises to form nitric acid. This is a two-stage reaction.

$$NH_3(g) + O_2(g) \rightleftharpoons NO(g) + H_2O(g)$$

$$NO(g) + O_2(g) + H_2O \rightleftharpoons HNO_3(g)$$

(i) Balance both of the equations above.
(2 marks)

(ii) Ammonia and nitric acid are reacted together to make ammonium nitrate, which is commonly used as a fertiliser. Write a chemical equation for this reaction.

....
(1 mark)

(iii) Briefly describe **one** way in which ammonium nitrate can have a harmful effect on the environment if used in excessive quantities.

....

....
(2 marks)

Leave blank

CHP42

GCSE

Double Science (Coordinated)

Chemistry

Answer Book

Practice Exam Papers

Higher Tier

These practice papers won't make you better at science

... but they will show you what you **can** do, and what you **can't** do.

These are GCSE papers, just like you'll get in your exams — so they'll tell you what you need to **work at** if you want to do **better** on the day.

Do an exam, **mark it** and look at what you **got wrong**.
That's the stuff you need to learn.

Go away, **learn** those tricky bits, then **do the same exam again**. If you're **still** getting questions wrong, you'll have to do even **more practice** and **keep testing** yourself until you keep getting **all** the questions right.

It doesn't sound like a lot of **fun**, but it **really will help**.

The three big ways to improve your score

1) **Answer all these exams**
These practice papers contain all the types of question that have come up year after year in GCSE exams. If you can do all these, you should be able to do all the questions in your exams.

2) **Keep practising the things you get wrong**
The whole point of a practice exam is to find out what you don't know*. So every time you get a question wrong, revise that subject then have another crack at it.
*Use the mark scheme in this booklet to help you see where you dropped your marks.

3) **Don't throw away easy marks**
Always answer the question the way it's asked — if it asks for symbols, don't use the chemical names. Always double-check your answer and don't make silly mistakes — obvious really.

Remember: the fewer marks you lose, the more marks you get.

Working out your Grade

- In the real exam, you'll do one Physics, one Biology and one Chemistry paper. This pack contains practice Chemistry papers.
- Use the answers and mark scheme to mark each paper. The marks are all out of 100, so they're already percentages.
- If you've done papers in Physics and Biology as well, find your average percentage for the whole exam.
- Look up your mark in this table to see what grade you got. If you're borderline, don't push yourself up a grade — the real examiners won't.

Average %	85+	74 – 84	61 – 73	47 – 60	37 – 46	30 – 36	under 30
Grade	**A***	**A**	**B**	**C**	**D**	**E**	**U**

Stick your marks in here so you can see how you're doing

(We've included space for your Physics and Biology results as well.)

		Physics	Chemistry	Biology	Average %	Grade
EXAM 1	First go					
	Second go					
	Third go					
EXAM 2	First go					
	Second go					
	Third go					
EXAM 3	First go					
	Second go					
	Third go					

Important!

Any grade you get on one of these practice papers is **no guarantee** of getting that in the real exam — **but** it's a pretty good guide.

Chemistry Paper 1 — Higher Tier

1 **(a)**

	number of protons	number of neutrons	number of electrons	electron arrangement
Potassium-39	19	20	19	2, 8, 8, 1
Chlorine-35	17	18	17	2, 8, 7

[1 mark for getting potassium completely correct; 1 mark for getting the number of protons and electrons for chlorine correct, and 1 mark for the correct electron arrangement for chlorine].

(b) ***Potassium loses its outside electron*** [1 mark], so a potassium ion K^+ is formed, with electron configuration ***2, 8, 8***, and charge +1.
Chlorine gains this electron [1 mark], so a chlorine ion Cl^- is formed, with electron configuration ***2, 8, 8***, charge –1.
[1 mark if you get both of the electron configurations (in bold) correct].
These oppositely charged ions are then ***attracted to each other*** [1 mark] to form potassium chloride KCl.

(c) The bond in Ca^{2+} O^{2-} is ***stronger*** than that in K^+ Cl^- because both the ions have twice the charge [1 mark], so it needs ***more energy, and hence a higher temperature, to break*** this bond [1 mark].

An easy start... just to ease you in gently... ah... electron structure... that feels good...

---

2 **(a)** ***Plants and animals died*** millions of years ago [1 mark], and were ***covered with sediment*** [1 mark]. Millions of years of ***pressure and heat*** then changed these remains into crude oil [1 mark].

(b) **(i)** Fractional distillation [1 mark].

(ii) Crude oil is ***heated*** [1 mark], and the vapour rises up the fractionating column until the temperature falls to its boiling point. ***Fractions with different boiling points can be tapped off in different places*** [1 mark].

The money you can make digging up dead plants and stuff. Who'd have thought...

---

3 **(a)** **(i)** Group 7 [1 mark].

(ii) The halogens [1 mark].

(iii) The 4th period [1 mark].

(iv) 35 [1 mark] (= 2 + 8 + 18 + 7, the total number of electrons / protons).

(v) 80 [1 mark]. (Use the Periodic Table.)

(vi) Bromine; Br [1 mark for both correct].

(b) **(i)** –1 [1 mark for the negative sign, 1 mark for the number 1]

(ii) Fluorine, chlorine, iodine or astatine [1 mark for any of these].

(c) 1. They are ***poor conductors of heat***.

2. They ***do not conduct electricity*** (except graphite).

3. They are ***non-shiny*** when solid.

4. They generally have ***low melting and boiling points***.

[1 mark each for any two of these].

---

4 **(a)** ***New layers are formed by deposition on top of existing layers*** [1 mark], so ***deeper layers are likely to have been there the longest*** [1 mark].

Considering this is Chemistry, I think this stuff is quite interesting.

(b) Evolution means that ***life is continually changing*** (evolving) [1 mark], and so similar kinds of fossil are ***good evidence that they were buried at the same*** time [1 mark], and hence that the rocks are about the same age.

Okay, I take your point... it's not as good as eating cake...

(c) Metamorphic [1 mark].

... but compared to some of the other stuff... well... this ain't so bad.

(d) The ***high temperatures*** that melt the rock to form magma destroy any fossils that may have been present [1 mark].

(e) ***Intrusive igneous rocks cool and become solid underground***, whereas ***extrusive igneous rocks become solid above ground*** [1 mark]. This means that intrusive igneous rocks ***cool much more slowly*** [1 mark], which results in ***bigger crystals*** than are found in extrusive igneous rocks [1 mark].

---

5 **(a)** Exothermic [1 mark].

(b) **(i)** The amount of ***heat (energy) given out*** in the reaction (i.e. the energy transfer ΔH) [1 mark].

(ii) It takes a certain ***amount of energy to break the bonds*** in the reactants [1 mark], while a certain ***amount of energy is given out*** when bonds are formed in the products [1 mark]. The quantity x is the difference between these two energies (i.e. the energy released in bond formation minus the energy needed for bond breaking) [1 mark].

It's not like some stuff where you have to remember millions of separate reactions. Spend some time... understand it... and you'll be okay.

[1 mark for the right number of bonds between the atoms (apart from the outer ones), and 1 mark for the correct structure.] (You don't have to draw quite so many atoms as here — as long as the structure is clear.)

(ii) There are four marks available for writing about ***two*** of the following properties — you get 1 for a property and 1 mark for its explanation.

It has a ***high melting point*** and a ***high boiling point*** [1 mark for either], as the ***bonds between the atoms are strong and it takes a lot of energy to break them*** [1 mark].

It is ***insoluble in water*** [1 mark], as the ***bonds are strong*** [1 mark] (and non-polar).

It is ***very rigid*** [1 mark] due to the ***strong bonds*** between the carbon atoms [1 mark].

It ***does not conduct electricity*** [1 mark], as there are ***no free electrons*** to carry an electric current [1 mark].

Diamonds are a girl's best friend. This is due to the giant covalent structure. Discuss.

---

3 (a) $Mg\ (s) + 2\ HCl\ (aq) \longrightarrow MgCl_2\ (aq) + H_2\ (g)$ [1 mark].

(b) (i) The acid was ***in excess*** — there was more acid than was needed to react with all the magnesium [1 mark].

(ii) ***Concentration*** (of the acid) [1 mark].

(iii)

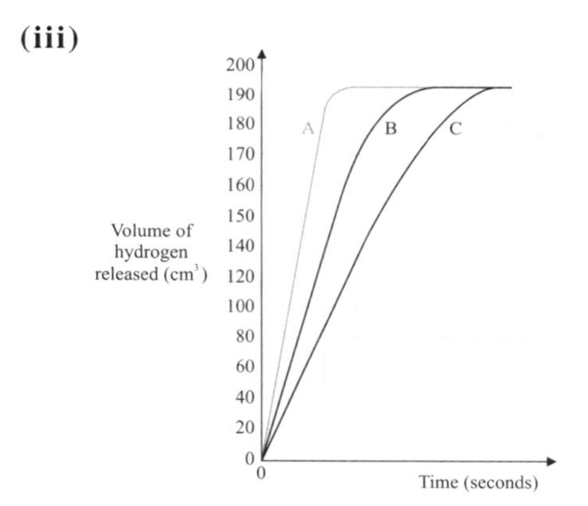

[1 mark for each curve correct, but they must finish at the same height]. (It doesn't matter if they're a bit more curved at the top.)

(c) Choose any ***two*** of the following:

Increase the temperature [1 mark]. More energy ***increases the speed*** of the molecules, which means more collisions. Also, a higher temperature means ***more collisions are made with enough energy*** to cause a reaction [1 mark for either reason].

Chop up the magnesium ribbon to ***increase the surface area*** [1 mark]. This larger surface area means there is ***more magnesium in contact with the acid*** molecules [1 mark], and so more collisions.

Add a catalyst [1 mark]. These ***reduce the energy needed*** for a collision to be successful [1 mark], (i.e. they reduce the activation energy).

---

4 **(a)** **(i)** Exothermic [1 mark]. The ***products have less energy*** than the reactants, and this "spare" energy is given out as heat. [1 mark].

(ii) B [1 mark].

(iii) C [1 mark].

(b) **(i)** ***Platinum***, ***palladium*** or ***rhodium*** [1 mark for any of these].

(ii) $2CO + O_2 \longrightarrow 2CO_2$

[1 mark for the correct reactants and products, plus an extra mark if the equation is correctly balanced].

(c) They can ***save money***, as the plant can work at lower temperatures and pressures [1 mark]. (So it's cheaper to build and less expensive to run.)

They can ***save time***, as the products can be made more quickly [1 mark].

---

5 **(a)** ***Layers of sediment are laid down*** in lakes and seas [1 mark]. Then as more sediment builds up, ***pressure*** squeezes out the water [1 mark], and the ***particles stick together*** as the salts crystallise [1 mark]. (Sedimentary rocks can also be formed from chemical deposition, or from organic material, like in the case of coal.)

(b) Limestone / chalk [1 mark]. (Although strictly speaking, chalk is mostly formed from microscopic lime-secreting algae.)

(c) Metamorphic [1 mark].

---

6 **(a)** Work out the number of moles in 100 g of the compound, then it's easy to see the ratio of the three elements.

Moles of carbon in 100 g of the compound = 9.9 ÷ 12 = 0.825.

Moles of fluorine in 100 g of the compound = 31.4 ÷ 19 = 1.653.

Moles of chlorine in 100 g of the compound = 58.7 ÷ 35.5 = 1.654.

So the ratio of moles in the compound is 0.825 : 1.653 :1.654 ≅ 1 : 2 : 2 [1 mark]. So the formula of the compound must be CF_2Cl_2 [1 mark].

(b) **(i)** CFCs are broken down by the Sun's radiation, which releases chlorine atoms (radicals) [1 mark], which destroy ozone in the ozone layer [1 mark].

(ii) Ultraviolet light can cause skin cancer and cataracts [1 mark for either of these].

(c) **(i)** Carbon dioxide (CO_2) [1 mark].

(ii) The increased temperature could ***melt polar ice*** and cause a ***rise in the sea-level***. It could also ***cause climate change*** with ***more extreme weather*** conditions, which in turn could cause ***droughts***, ***desertification*** and ***crop failures*** [2 marks available — get a mark for expressing any of the ideas in bold].

---

7 **(a)** A lower temperature is required [1 mark], so it is cheaper.

If ever you need to guess why something is done a certain way in industry — a good place to start is by saying that it's cheaper or more efficient.

(b) The ***carbon reacts*** and is ***converted to carbon dioxide*** (CO_2) [1 mark for either idea].

(c) At the anode: $2\,O^{2-} \longrightarrow O_2 + 4\,e^-$.
At the cathode: $Al^{3+} + 3e^- \longrightarrow Al$.
[1 mark for each equation for getting the ions and electrons right, and an extra mark if both equations are balanced.]

(d) The process needs high temperatures, which requires a lot of electricity [1 mark].

(e) Choose any *three* of the following: ***resistant to corrosion***, ***strong***, ***lightweight***, ***easily shaped*** [1 mark each].

---

8 (a) (i) ***Electrical cables***, because it's ***easily bent*** and is a ***good conductor*** of electricity.
Cooking pots, because it's a ***good conductor of heat*** and is ***unreactive***.
Plumbing, because it's ***easily shaped*** and is ***unreactive***.
[1 mark for a use, and 1 mark for an explanation.]

(ii) ***Plating*** car bumpers etc., because it's very ***shiny*** and ***resistant to rust***.
Used in ***stainless steel***, because it ***strengthens iron*** and ***makes it more resistant to corrosion***.
Used as a ***catalyst*** (because it's a good catalyst).
[1 mark for a use, and 1 mark for an explanation.]

(b) Pretty much any two gemstones, e.g. emerald, sapphire, ruby, topaz, amethyst, opal, aquamarine [1 mark each up to a maximum of 2].

(c) $4\,Fe\,(s) + 3\,O_2 \longrightarrow 2\,Fe_2O_3$
[1 mark for Fe_2O_3, and 1 mark for a correctly balanced equation].

(d) Nickel is ***much less reactive*** than sodium [1 mark], and so coins made from nickel will ***last longer*** than coins made from sodium [1 mark]. In fact, Group I metals are so reactive that coins made from them would be ***dangerous*** [1 mark].

---

9 (a)

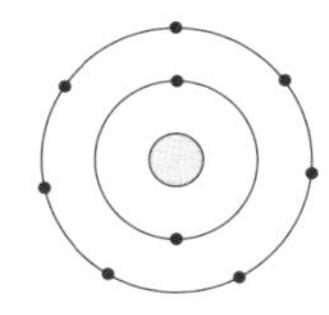

i.e. 2 electrons in the first shell and 7 in the second [1 mark].

(b) (i) 193 + 159 = ***352*** kJ/mol [1 mark].

(ii) Breaking the bromine and fluorine bonds takes 352 kJ. When the Br – F bonds are formed, 208 kJ of energy are released, so there must be ***352 + 208 = 560 kJ*** [1 mark for this calculation] of energy in the bonds of two moles of bromine fluoride. This means the bond energy per mole is ***560 ÷ 2 = 280 kJ*** [2 marks, but lose 1 mark if you forgot to divide by 2 and gave the answer as 560 kJ/mol].

(c) (i) Fluorine's used in toothpaste and drinking water to ***prevent tooth decay***; it's used to make ***refrigerants*** and ***other chemicals***, and in ***etching glass*** [1 mark for any one correct use].

(ii) Chlorine is ***used in swimming pools*** and ***drinking water*** etc. to kill bacteria and other bugs; it is used to make ***bleach***, ***insecticides***, ***HCl*** and ***other chemicals*** [1 mark for any one correct use].